TOO MANY PANTS

Written by Ruth Drury
Illustrated by Ali Scothern
Published by LMD Publications
Printed by Stephens and George Print Group

"I am not going to school, I am staying at home with you!" shouted Lilidee, with an enormous frown on her face.

Lilidee was a small girl with BIG feelings.

But the problem with having BIG feelings in a little body, they sometimes get in a muddle.

"Oh dear Lilidee, you sound so unhappy today, I wonder what is wrong?" asked mum.

"Not telling you, GO AWAY!" shouted Lilidee with tears in her eyes.

Lilidee hated being angry with her mum but she felt so awful inside. The shouting just exploded out of her like a rocket.

"I wonder if it is because you can't find your socks?"
"I wonder if it is because Daddy snores?"

"Or I wonder if the problem is that you maybe
have too many pants on?" suggested mum.

Lilidee giggled. It was very funny
to hear her mum talking about pants!
"What do you mean Mum?
I only have one pair of pants on!" replied Lilidee,
who sat down next to her mum looking confused.

"Well Lilidee, every day, we all wear several pairs of pants, which are invisible to everyone except our own brains.

Mum wears helpful pants, chef pants, work pants, loving pants, hug pants and happy pants. These pants help her through the day to do all the things she needs to do."

8

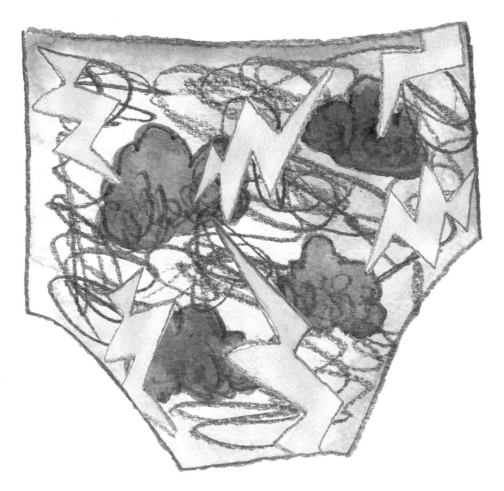

"However, sometimes when she is sleepy
or frustrated, her *grumpy* pants appear.
As do her *cross* pants, *moany* pants and even her *impatient*
pants which can make her day really tricky!" explained mum.

"Why don't you just not wear those pants mum? Just wear happy pants!" suggested Lilidee, cuddling into her mum.

"Well Lilidee, we are only in charge of which pants we take off. The problem is, they appear by themselves which is why your day can suddenly get harder."
"Your brain begins to have all of these strange feelings inside, whooshing around like a washing machine and before you know it – you have ANOTHER pair of pants on!"

"*Worried* pants, *nervous* pants, *scaredy* pants, *angry* pants, *cross* pants, *stubborn* pants, *excited* pants – all different kinds of pants which appear one after another, creating all sorts of muddled feelings inside your tummy."

Lilidee looked very worried.
She didn't know what she should do about all of
these pants which would be appearing on her.

"Telling adults, heavy blankets, favourite smells and baths.
Blowing bubbles, pulling faces – they're not just for laughs!

They scoot the pants away from you, as quickly as they came.
Then you can begin to think with a much calmer brain!"

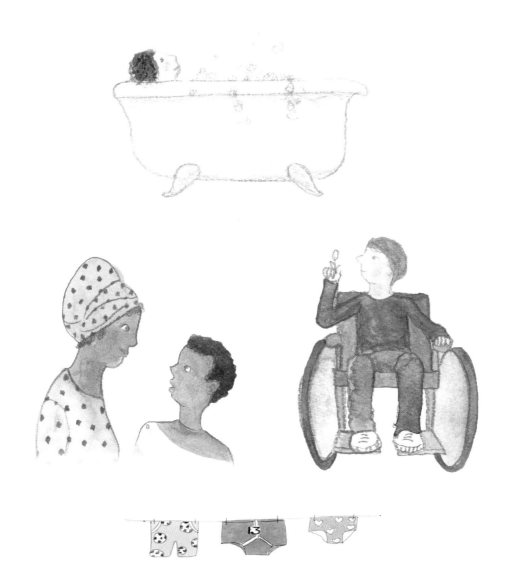

"The pants are great BIG feelings,
which make your tummy wriggle.
So, take them off, feel some love
and have a great big giggle!"
explained mum cuddling Lilidee closely.

"Wow!" Exclaimed Lilidee as she sat on mum's lap.
"It is so hard for me when my brain is whooshing
around and I have lots of feelings inside telling me what
to do! I didn't know it was up to me to
get rid of the tricky ones in that way!"

"Well, you can always ask someone for some help.
You never know, they might be wearing their hero pants
that day and just may have the right answer!" explained mum.

The End

"Hello! I am Ruth and I am really excited to have written this book.
I wrote it to help my own Lilidee understand that we all have too many pants which
make our tummies muddled. Even the big people in your life have this problem,
so maybe they need to think of all of their different pants too!"
"I am generally found at home with Nelly the dog, working, drawing or napping!
Or if the sun is shining I will be daydreaming of new story ideas in my beautiful garden,
in my hammock wearing flip-flops."